About the Book

This book starts with temperatures that are familiar to all of us, the temperatures of our bodies and our surroundings. It shows how vital it is, for example in a space research program, to be able to measure the maximum and minimum temperatures the body can endure. From here the scope of the book widens to range between the processes involved in measuring Absolute Zero on the thermometer and finding the temperatures of the nuclear fires that rage in the sun.

All science advances in tiny steps, the result of painstaking observation and measurement. The *Yardstick* books take some of the principal properties of matter which the scientist — whether chemist or engineer, materials scientist or plant pathologist — wants to measure. These properties are common to all science, so the authors draw their examples without reference to the classical divisions into "pure" and "applied" science. Each book extends across the widest range of its chosen property — in this book, from coldest to hottest.

YARDSTICKS OF SCIENCE

David Fishlock

Taking the temperature

Illustrated with photographs and drawings

Coward-McCann, Inc.   New York

Contents

Photographs

Figures

Preface

by David Fishlock

Science, once neatly split into the four great divisions of physics, chemistry, biology and mathematics, has become more and more fragmented. Today a bewildering 3,000 subspecies are distinguished — from astronomy and aerodynamics to wave mechanics and zoology.

A great deal of science is pursued for its own sake, with the aim, the romantic would have it, of pushing out the boundaries of knowledge (although one eminent modern scientist at least prefers to think of scientists "creeping along the boundaries with a magnifying glass"). Sometimes, as in the conquest of the moon or the unraveling of the life processes, many different disciplines are harnessed to a common purpose. But whether practiced for its own sake or as part of some grand design, all science advances in tiny steps, the result of painstaking observation and measurement by the scientist.

You are all familiar with some of these measurements; you use them every day — whenever you tell the time, check the temperature, glance at the speedometer. An American scientist has estimated recently that, by adding to all these casual measurements (perhaps up to fifty a day for every one of us) all those made in industry and by scientists, we arrive at a total of 20 billion measurements made *every day* in the United States alone.

The *Yardsticks of Science* introduce you to some of the principal properties of matter which the scientist — whether chemist or engineer, materials scientist or plant pathologist — wants to measure. These properties are common to all science, so Mr. Fishlock has drawn his examples without regard to the modern highly artificial division into "pure" and "applied" science. This book extends across the entire spectrum of its chosen property from coldest to hottest.

1 The world around us

One of the first things a doctor does when he sees a patient is to thrust a short glass thermometer into his mouth. Some people say he does this in order to keep the patient quiet while he thinks about the symptoms. But there is no doubt that the thermometer gives the doctor some very useful clues.

Perhaps you first heard the word "temperature" from your mother. You had complained of feeling hot and having a headache, and she put her hand on your forehead and declared that you were "running a temperature." She meant that your body's temperature, which normally remains remarkably steady within the very narrow range of 97 to 99 degrees Fahrenheit, had exceeded its normal limit. Usually the increase in temperature, to perhaps 100 to 102 degrees Fahrenheit, indicated that your body had been invaded by some harmful organism — had become infected, in other words — and the ensuing chemical battle in your bloodstream and at the site of the invasion had upset the body's very sensitive temperature control mechanism. (We are not sure, by the way, whether this rise in temperature is a help in defending the body, or whether it is the result of some partial breakdown in the body's temperature control system.)

Later on temperature took on another meaning, when you became aware of people's preoccupation with the weather. There is unceasing discussion of the weather on the radio and television, in the papers and in ordinary conversation. It indicates an interest that goes far beyond the real value to most of us of knowing what the weather is up to.

One reason for the interest, of course, is that in most parts of our country the weather is apt to change very suddenly; one can hardly imagine an Arab or an Eskimo being similarly preoccupied. Yet the range of temperatures we experience is really surprisingly narrow; much wider, it is true, than our body's own range, but still only occasionally outside the range $32°$ to $80°F$.

Beyond these limits, in both directions, there lies an enormous range of temperatures of which we can have little direct experience, simply because our bodies are not constructed to withstand them (Fig. 1). Even exposure to tropical sunshine at perhaps $110°F$. or to Arctic conditions at sub-zero temperatures can quickly prove disastrous to a person unaccustomed to them.

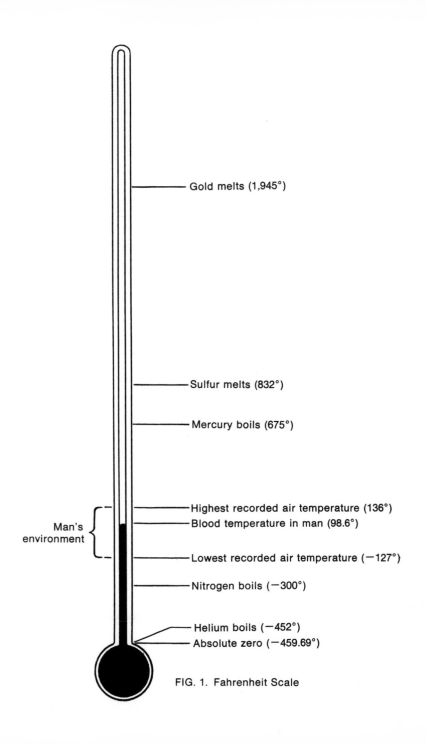

Gold melts (1,945°)

Sulfur melts (832°)

Mercury boils (675°)

Highest recorded air temperature (136°)
Blood temperature in man (98.6°)

Man's environment

Lowest recorded air temperature (−127°)

Nitrogen boils (−300°)

Helium boils (−452°)
Absolute zero (−459.69°)

FIG. 1. Fahrenheit Scale

People who inhabit these regions often have special protection. The Negro, for example, has a highly pigmented or dark-colored skin which prevents his body absorbing too much of the more harmful rays from the sun, especially the ultraviolet rays. The Eskimo, on the other hand, has extra layers of fat just beneath his skin to help keep out the cold. There are other differences, too, notably in their physical stature; where the Negro is tall, the Eskimo tends to be short and squat, and so offers a smaller area for radiating precious heat away from his body.

Even so, the highest and lowest air temperatures ever recorded on the earth's surface span a mere 263 degrees Fahrenheit. The highest, recorded at San Luis in Mexico on August 11, 1933, is 136°F.; the lowest, recorded at Vostok in the Antarctic on August 24, 1960, is −127°F. Yet everyone is familiar with temperatures well outside this range — very hot things like an oven, an electric heater and the filament of the electric light bulb.

So the next question is whether there are, in fact, any limits at all to temperature. Well, there is a very well-defined bottom limit to temperature. The lowest temperature we can possibly achieve is −459°F. Scientists in a laboratory at Oxford University in England have come within about a millionth of a degree of this incredibly low temperature — a thousand times farther down the absolute scale than the sun's inside temperature is up the scale. Just why we cannot get below it is explained in Chapter 2, where we shall be discussing the meaning of temperature.

Although there is a lower limit, there can be no upper limit to the temperature spectrum or scale of temperatures.

The hottest thing nature achieves on earth is the core of the earth itself, which geophysicists believe consists of a ball of molten material, metallic in its properties (iron, perhaps, or a mineral that behaves like iron under the fantastic pressure that exists there), a thousand miles in diameter, at a temperature of several thousand degrees Fahrenheit. Under normal conditions this molten core would have vaporized or boiled away, but it is contained by the immense strength of the earth's crust, a layer of rock many miles deep.

The sun, however, is an immense ball of intensely hot gas, even the outermost layers of which have a temperature of about 12,000°F. Although only a tiny fraction of all the heat radiated from this fiery globe reaches the earth's surface, this heat is responsible for the existence of all living things on the earth's surface.

Men have devised many ways of obtaining and using high temperatures, however, some of which are commonplace in every home. For example, the electric heater has a red-hot element which is normally at a temperature of about 1,800°F., while the electric light bulb gives out light because it has a filament or coil of fine wire which glows at around 3,000° or 4,000°F. Even the ordinary gas stove is capable of a temperature of several hundred degrees. A cigarette, glowing bright red as the smoker inhales, brings a temperature approaching 1,500°F. within an inch or so of his lips.

The spectrum of temperature is therefore enormously wide, stretching from absolute zero (-459°F.) to the sort of temperatures attained at the center of the sun, or briefly in a hydrogen bomb explosion (many millions of degrees). Almost every kind of scientist — chemist, physicist, meteorologist, engineer, doctor, and so on — is constantly interested in temperature, and in ways of measuring it more accurately (see Photo 1). Chapter 2 will show us why.

Man as an engine

Professor F. G. Young, a famous British biochemist, has observed wryly that the chief consequence of human activity is hot air. About three-quarters of the energy developed by our bodies is given off as heat.

The human body is essentially an engine, although a very complicated one. One of its most interesting aspects is its low working temperature. Whereas a gas turbine burns its fuel continuously at 1,000°C. (1,800°F.) or more, and diesel engines may reach peak temperatures beyond 2,000°C. (3,600°F.), the human body works at a temperature below 100°F. Even at rest, however, a man will have an energy output of about one-fifteenth of one horsepower, which may rise nearly tenfold if he does strenuous work.

This energy is generated by the combustion of fuel in the foods we eat, using the oxygen in the air we inhale as the *oxidizing agent.* This mechanism precisely parallels the reaction of gasoline or diesel fuel with oxygen (again from the air), except that the latter takes place with an explosive violence that would soon destroy a living engine like the human body.

A man at rest will burn up about 18 quarts of oxygen an hour to consume the three principal ingredients of our food — carbohydrates (such as bread and potatoes), fats (such as butter), and proteins (such as fish and meat). This highly

PHOTO 1. Claimed to be the world's most versatile thermometer, this tiny temperature sensor, called a thermistor, can measure temperatures over a range from −325°F. to 1,200°F. As the temperature changes, so do the electrical properties of a small artificial diamond, enclosed in the glass bead. The praying mantis provides an idea of the thermistor's size.

intricate process of combustion, resulting in an output of mechanical energy, heat and fresh body tissue, is usually called the body's *metabolism* (Fig 2).

In order to sustain its temperature within about 1°C., despite a tenfold difference in energy output between rest and sustained effort, the body needs a remarkably efficient means for regulating temperature. This "thermostat" is located at the base of the skull and works on information received about the temperature of the blood and the skin. The action it can take, should the body's temperature begin to rise, is to increase the rate at which the body loses heat by evaporation of moisture from the skin (sweating). If the temperature should begin to fall, the skin itself will take action to reduce the heat lost from it, while the body itself may try to generate more heat by a spontaneous movement of muscles, which we call shivering, in an effort to increase its heat output.

By the same token, the human body is truly comfortable over a surprisingly narrow range of temperature. Indoors, the optimum temperature for a man at rest is about 64°F. to 69°F. The European engineers who designed the supersonic Concorde airliner had to balance the air-conditioning system carefully against the heat that streams in from a surface temperature over the airplane of 120°C. and the hot air that pours from its 138 passengers.

Much the same problem faced engineers in the United States responsible for the design of underground shelters from nuclear attack. The assumption here was that occupants might spend not two or three hours as they will in the Concorde but days or even weeks in the shelter. Yet economics would allot to each occupant no more than about 70 cubic feet of living space.

RESPIRATION

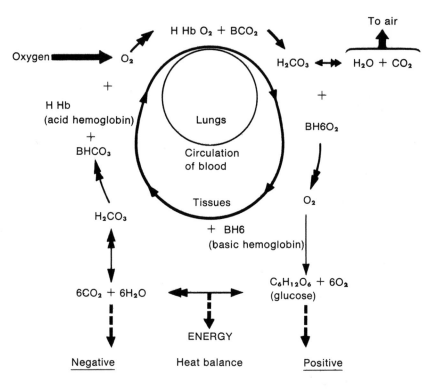

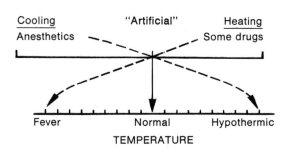

FIG. 2. Process of combustion known as metabolism

To learn more about living under congested conditions without exposing men to them, these engineers designed the simoc, or simulated occupant — a simple robot about four feet tall who sweated like a man. The simoc was, in fact, the thermodynamic equivalent of a man. One of the things demonstrated was that sweating kept the simoc "comfortable" until humidity, or moisture content of the surrounding air, reached a certain point. But beyond this point the simoc's temperature began to rise.

We shall later discuss what can happen to a human body that is giving up its heat too fast to the air around. No less disastrous are the consequences to a body unable to liberate heat to the surrounding air by sweating. Here also the body's temperature control system is hampered, and the body temperature begins to rise quite rapidly.

Whereas a naked man, in completely dry air indoors, can tolerate a temperature as high as $111°F.$ ($44°C.$) and a suitably clothed one as high as $138°F.$ ($59°C.$), man is far more vulnerable to a high humidity. When the air is saturated with water — that is, when the humidity is 100 percent — moisture can no longer evaporate from the skin. Under these conditions the temperature-regulating system of a clothed body goes out of control at $88°F.$ ($31°C.$) and that of a naked body at only 3 degrees Fahrenheit higher. The blood just cannot circulate fast enough to carry the heat away to the skin. The result is a fever, and an alarmingly sudden death by heat stroke if something isn't done quickly to stop the rise in temperature.

2 The meaning of temperature

Temperature is normally regarded as one of the four fundamental units of science, the others being mass, length and
time. Yet temperature is a different kind of unit altogether
from its companions. Whereas mass, length and time can be
regarded quite simply as *quantities*, temperature is strictly a
quality.

Let us look at this another way. If we put two lengths or
masses together or add two intervals of time, we obtain the
sum of their values. But this is not so with temperature. Put
two bricks, heated to the same temperature, one on top of the
other and take their temperature. It does not change.

The corresponding *quantity* is really heat — which is simply energy that is in the process of changing from one form to another. For example, the chemical energy of gasoline changes to the mechanical energy of a car's crankshaft by way of heat — the heat generated when gasoline is burned.

We can have a very small area of heat at a very high temperature, as we find in the glowing tip of a cigarette or the filament of a flashlight bulb. Or we can have a large area of heat at quite a modest temperature, as we have in a gas oven.

Once heat was believed to be a fluid which, under certain circumstances, could be liberated from any substance. The weakness of this theory was that there seemed to be no limit to the amount of this hypothetical fluid — variously known as *caloric* or *phlogiston* — that a substance might contain. This was hard to explain away. It led to the idea that heat was really some form of energy — in fact, of motion between the atoms of the substance.

From this we might reason that if heat is a measure of atomic activity — the greater the amount of activity, the greater the amount of heat involved — then temperature must be the speed of the activity. In other words, it must be a measure of how frantically the atoms in a substance are dashing about. We might also deduce that there is a point at which all agitation ceases among the atoms.

How hot?

Scientists were slow to appreciate the value of measuring temperature. While the Egyptians who designed the Great

Pyramid 4,600 years ago could measure length with an accuracy better than one part in 1,000, and Chaldean astronomers were able to measure time to at least one part in 10,000, no one bothered to measure temperature at all until the Middle Ages. Galileo then invented his *thermoscope,* which we shall speak about later.

Since temperature cannot be measured in absolute terms, it must be defined in terms of a scale, which requires at least two fixed points of reference. The first scientifically acceptable scale was that of the German scientist, Daniel Gabriel Fahrenheit, who in 1726 proposed a scale based on the melting point of ice and the temperature of a healthy human body, to which he assigned the values of $32°$ and $96°$, respectively.

The standard scale used by scientists today, however, is the one proposed by the Swedish astronomer Anders Celsius, professor of astronomy at Uppsala University in 1742. He called it the Centigrade scale, since it divides the difference in temperature between the boiling and freezing points of water into exactly 100 degrees. (In 1948 this scale was officially renamed the Celsius scale, and it is now known by this name, among scientists at least.)

In 1927 an international committee defined a very accurate standard scale of temperature known as the International Practical Scale of Temperature, or I.P.S.T., arranged to conform as closely as possible with the Celsius scale. This I.P.S.T. is constantly revised as methods of measuring temperature are improved by work in the standards division of such laboratories as the National Physical Laboratory at Teddington in Britain and the National Bureau of Standards in Washington. In particular there is great interest in extending the upper and lower limits of the I.P.S.T., especially as these extremes of temperature grow more and more important industrially.

The Kelvin scale of temperature, frequently used among scientists, was proposed by William Thomson, later Lord Kelvin. Its lower reference point is absolute zero, that point at which all molecular agitation is believed to cease. Starting the scale from this point has the supreme merit that we need no longer worry about negative values of temperature — everything now has a positive value of some temperature on this scale. On the Kelvin scale, water freezes at $273.16\,^{\circ}K$ (Fig. 3.)

Pure substances usually have very accurately defined melting points and boiling points. The chemist can use this fact to help identify a substance once he has purified it sufficiently. The physicist has adopted certain substances, in addition to water, as standards, having measured their melting points extremely accurately. They include:

Hydrogen	boiling point	$20.267\,^{\circ}K$
Oxygen	boiling point	$90.17\,^{\circ}K$
Sulfur	melting point	$444.6\,^{\circ}C$
Gold	melting point	$1,063\,^{\circ}C$

From now on we drop the Fahrenheit scale of Fig. 1, and use only the Centigrade (Celsius) scale for temperature, as scientists do, except in Chapter 4. To avoid using negative values of temperature, we will specify very low temperatures on the Kelvin scale. The two boiling points in the list above are given in degrees Kelvin; in degrees Centigrade, hydrogen boils at -253, hydrogen at -182.9.

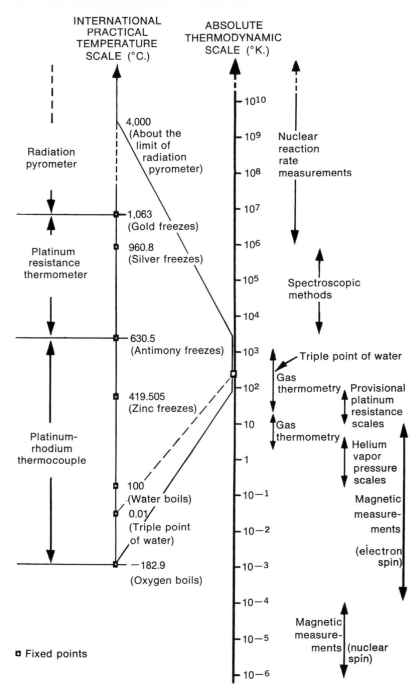

FIG. 3. International Practical Temperature Scale (Centigrade), and Absolute Thermodynamic Scale (Kelvin)

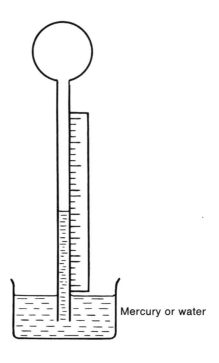

Mercury or water

FIG. 4. Galileo's therometer, designed about 1600

Thermometers

How, then, can we measure the speed of atomic activity —
or temperature? One way is to measure the expansion of some
suitable fluid as it gets hotter and its atoms demand more and
more room.

The first thermometer was invented by Galileo about 1600.
It is sketched in Fig. 4. The bulb was inverted over a bath of
mercury or water. It relied upon the air temperature outside
the bulb expanding or contracting the air within, so that the

level of liquid *fell* with increasing temperature. (This is in contrast to an ordinary modern thermometer, in which the liquid itself is expanded by the air temperature outside.) Unfortunately, Galileo's instrument was inaccurate, for it was influenced by both temperature and atmospheric pressure. In fact, it is more accurately called a *thermoscope* than a *thermometer,* for it displays temperature rather than measures it.

Sanctorius, a professor of medicine at Padua and a friend of Galileo, modified this instrument for clinical use, and published an account of his work in 1612. The instrument now consisted of a long glass tube, with several bends in it, open at one end and sealed by a bulb at the other. When the bulb was warmed and the open end immersed in water, the tube partially filled. If, then, the bulb were placed in a patient's mouth, a different water level was obtained, which provided a crude measure of the patient's temperature.

More significant in many ways than the instrument itself was the work Sanctorius published thirteen years later, demonstrating the value of temperature measurement in the diagnosis of disease. But his revolutionary ideas were soon forgotten, not to be revived for another two centuries, when less clumsy versions of the clinical thermometer began to appear. The first may have been the ten-inch instrument made for William Aitkin in 1852. But it was Sir Thomas Allbutt, in 1867, who designed the first practical thermometer, forerunner of the instrument carried today by every nurse.

The modern clinical thermometer is a slender glass tube, a few inches in length, the bore of which is very fine, to amplify as much as possible very small changes in the volume of its contents. It looks wider because one side of the tube bulges slightly so that, when examined from the front, the thread of mercury it contains is magnified to make the reading easier.

Its scale stretches from 35° to 42°C. (95° to 108°F.), comfortably beyond the likely limits of fluctuation in body temperature. This instrument is normally left in place — in the patient's mouth or in the rectum, for example — for about half a minute (compared with twenty minutes for Aitkin's ten-inch model). When the thermometer is removed, a small constriction in the bore holds the thread of mercury in place while the temperature is read off. A sharp shake then returns the mercury to the bulb.

This kind of mercury-in-glass thermometer has a much wider span than body temperature, of course, and can be designed to register temperature within a tenth of a degree over any portion of the scale from −30° to +500° Centigrade. Lower temperatures can be measured by filling the instrument with colored alcohol instead of mercury, which extends its range downward to about −100°C., although the upper limit is then only 30°C.

This kind of thermometer responds very quickly to temperature changes and despite its fragility is most convenient to use. But petty errors can creep in, usually through small irregularities in the volume of the glass tube. Some countries have standards laboratories where a good glass thermometer can be *calibrated* or checked against a very accurately known temperature (Photo 2).

But often the scientist needs a more precise means of measuring temperature. There are many other kinds of thermom-

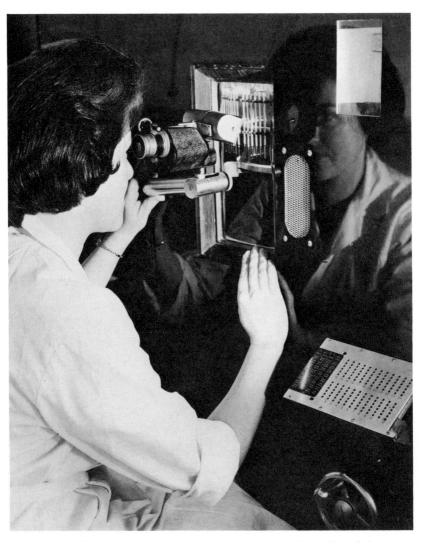

PHOTO 2. Technician checks the accuracy of a batch of clinical thermometers against a standard thermometer.

eters, mostly of special application. The most important, precise method, over a wide range of temperature from $-200°$ to $1,200°$C., is to measure the way a piece of pure platinum changes in electrical resistance (the resistance to the passage of electric current) with the change in temperature (Fig. 5).

A well-prepared piece of platinum will register temperatures up to 500°C. with an accuracy of one hundredth of a degree, and temperatures as high as 1,300°C. (near the melting point of iron) with an accuracy of a tenth of a degree. There is one catch, however — the method is sluggish, so the *resistance thermometer* cannot follow temperatures that change quickly. But usually the scientist is more concerned with accuracy than with speed.

Rays of heat

Everything above absolute zero emits heat waves, or infrared waves, which we detect as heat in bodies warmer than our own. Infrared waves, as the name suggests, lie below the visible red waves on the scale of electromagnetic radiation; that is, their wavelength is longer than 0.75 microns, the longest the human eye can detect, and may reach 1 millimeter or more. When an object becomes very hot, above 500°C., it also begins to emit visible light and to glow first dull red, then bright red, and eventually white-hot.

The first infrared detector was an ordinary glass thermometer. In 1800, Sir William Herschel, the court astronomer of England, used the thermometer to demonstrate that the sun emitted rays which, although invisible, would generate heat

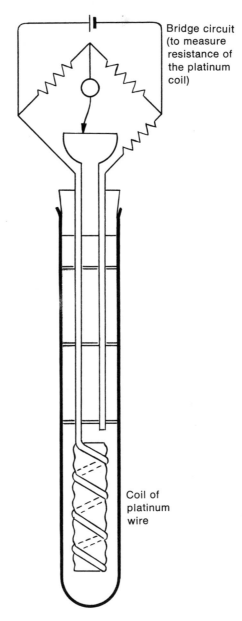

Bridge circuit (to measure resistance of the platinum coil)

Coil of platinum wire

FIG. 5. A resistance thermometer

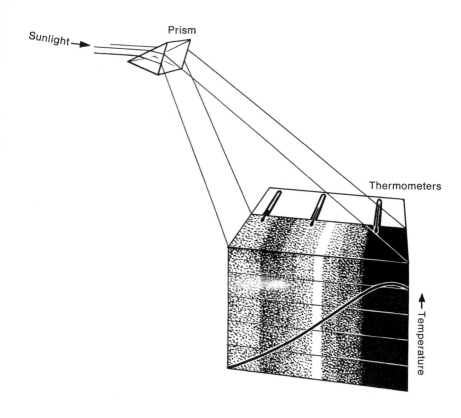

FIG. 6. Infrared detector used by Sir William Herschel in 1800

(Fig. 6). Modern infrared detectors have a much quicker response, however. The latest kinds of electronic eye can detect many infrared wavelengths and can also convert what they see into visible rays, so that we can now observe quite cool bodies by the heat rays they give off.

Just how valuable an ability to "see" heat can be was demonstrated during the Second World War. While some governments encouraged people to eat carrots, on the unlikely grounds that they helped fighter pilots to see at night (the real reason was that they were home-grown and freely available), scientists were at work on more practical aids to night vision. The result was such devices as infrared periscopes and binoculars, that enabled a watching soldier to observe a pitch-black battlefield and see men and vehicles outlined by their own heat waves.

Variations in the temperature of an object can also be detected very precisely in this way and can be used to locate malfunctioning in an engineering assembly or a human body, for example. Highly sensitive infrared cameras have recently been developed that allow the doctor to photograph, say, a leg or a chest and detect areas of inflammation only a few hundredths of a degree hotter than the surrounding tissue. The technique is proving valuable in the detection of certain cancers earlier than X-rays can show them and in the examination of pregnant women who may be harmed by X-rays.

The heat camera builds up its picture by recording the heat waves that emanate from many thousands of separate points on the surface being examined. These "temperatures" are then reconstructed, rather like a television picture, into a pattern of gray shades — the darker the gray, the cooler the temperature. By this technique, called *thermography,* the United States Air Force, while investigating arctic clothing, has photographed a man clad only in shorts in a refrigerator at freezing point. This showed, for instance, that different parts of the body cool at different rates (see Photo 3). The

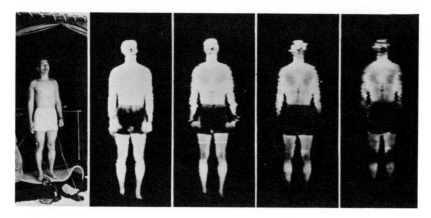

PHOTO 3. Thermograms made by the U.S. Air Force's Department of Protective Equipment reveal changes in the skin temperature of a partly clad man exposed to freezing weather. Exposure time increases from left to right. The dark areas are those from which heat is lost most rapidly.

knees cool quickly but the neck much more slowly; moreover, the body cools much more rapidly once below 4.4°C. (40°F.) — a fact now known to bring about the disastrous descent in body temperature that can afflict walkers and climbers who have become wet and tired (see Chapter 4).

Elsewhere the emission of heat rays has allowed scientists to take thermograms that show overheating in the walls of a blast furnace or in the pipes of a steam plant for generating electricity. It allows electronic engineers to examine an electrical circuit and see how the heat (and hence the current) is distributed. An *infrared micrometer* now allows the steelmaker to position the edge of a length of red-hot steel literally within a hair's breadth as it emerges from the rollers of the steel mill at over thirty miles an hour.

In space, too, infrared waves are a valuable source of information. Infrared radiometers aboard the *Mariner II* spacecraft told us that the clouds which blanket the planet Venus have a temperature that varies from about −30°C. to −50°C.

If we hang a thermometer in the sun on a hot summer's day, it may rise as high as 25–35 °C. But every schoolboy will know of one way in which he can obtain a very much higher temperature from the sun's rays. A magnifying glass concentrates the rays falling upon it to a very small spot, the temperature of which can easily become high enough to ignite

FIG. 7. Variations in temperature of the cloud blanket surrounding Venus, shown by infrared radiometers

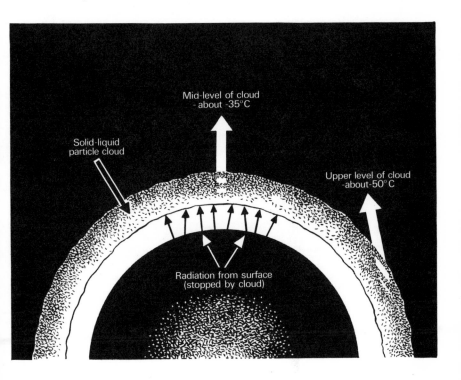

Mid-level of cloud - about -35°C

Upper level of cloud -about-50° C

Solid-liquid particle cloud

Radiation from surface (stopped by cloud)

combustible materials such as paper or wood. Acres of parched scrubland have been set alight by the sun shining through the bottom of a broken bottle. The same principle is used in the solar furnace, where a large area of sunshine is focused to one point — which may reach a temperature of 6,000°C., high enough to melt any substance.

Conduction and convection

Radiation, then, is one way by which heat can be transferred from one place to another — a very important way, as it happens, for this is the sole means by which the sun's heat reaches the earth. There are two other methods by which heat can be transferred, but neither can operate across the 93 million miles of empty space that separate us from the sun.

Both these methods rely on the presence of molecules of some substance — solid, liquid or gas — to convey the heat.

One of the fundamental laws of science tells us that heat will flow from a hot body to a cooler one — but not in the opposite direction. If we place a cool body in contact with a hot one — for example, a leg of lamb in a hot oven — the lively hot air molecules will immediately start to bang against the meat, causing some of the molecules of lamb to vibrate faster too. The longer the meat remains in the oven, the faster its molecules will vibrate, until the meat reaches the same temperature as the air in the oven.

This mode of "heat transfer," to use a technical expression commonly employed by engineers, is called *conduction*. A very commonplace example is the warming of the teapot by rinsing it out with hot water before we make a pot of tea.

Some of the heat is transferred from the water to the pot, and the water we throw away will be appreciably cooler than it was when we put it in.

Different substances vary enormously in their ability to conduct heat. Normally a substance that will conduct electricity well, such as a metal, will also conduct heat rapidly. A material which is a poor conductor of heat, such as glass or paper, is also a poor conductor of electricity. Air, too, is a poor conductor of heat, which is why we wear several layers of clothes on a cold day. Between each a layer of air is trapped, preventing the heat our body is emitting from being lost to the air around us, and thus creating our own microclimate. Double-paned windows prevent loss of heat from a room because a layer of air is trapped between the two glass panels. In each case, if the air were not trapped and held still, it would quickly transfer heat from the hotter to the cooler region.

The last mode in which heat is transferred is called *convection*. Convection is a means of heat transfer peculiar to fluids — that is, to liquids and gases — but not to solids. Unlike solids, fluids have no rigid structure, and their molecules are quite mobile. As they become hotter and therefore more agitated, they tend to fly farther apart. In consequence, as you might expect, the substance becomes lighter, for there will be fewer molecules in a given volume. And, being lighter, the warm fluid will tend to move upward, to rise.

This apparently insignificant movement of the warmer zones within a mass of fluid is responsible for some pretty important events. For example, one reason why Bermuda has a milder climate than nearby states on the mainland of America is because of a continuous movement of warm water from the Gulf of Mexico across the Atlantic Ocean which flows near the island of Bermuda. This *convection current*, as the scientists call it, is known as the Gulf Stream, a warm current some eighty miles across.

Convection currents are responsible, in fact, for most of the world's weather. Put at its simplest, the air above the hottest regions of the world, around the equator, becomes heated and starts to rise, allowing cooler air currents to pour in beneath. But above the polar regions, where the earth is very cold, the opposite movement of air is taking place. Thus we have two massive air movements occurring simultaneously around our planet. At the same time the earth is rotating very rapidly, a process that disturbs these air currents. Here then is the basic mechanism for the "weather machine."

Warm air currents, or winds, sweeping across the sea evaporate some of the water and carry it to the land masses. If these land masses are cooler than the air above them, the air currents will be cooled by them. Cool air can retain less moisture than warm air, so the likelihood is that the air will relinquish some of its moisture as rain or snow or hail. Attempts to control the weather by making clouds relinquish their rain above land that is too warm to cool the air itself have so far consisted of spraying fine crystals of ice from an airplane on top of the clouds.

There is a rather terrifying piece of weather, known variously as the hurricane or the typhoon or the cyclone (depending on which part of the world you live in), that appears to depend on both conduction and convection for its existence. It starts — no one is quite sure how — over the warm oce-

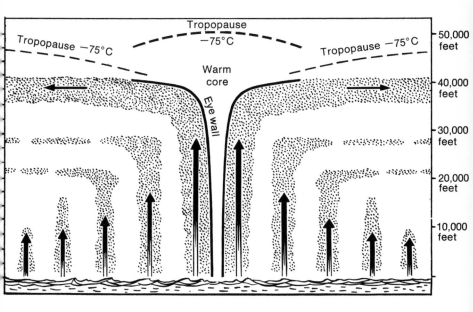

FIG. 8. How a typhoon is formed

anic regions in the tropics. A swirling wind suddenly begins
to transfer heat from the warm sea, 27°C. or more, into the
air at a phenomenal rate. Extremely quickly there arises a
mighty column of air that is sucking heat from the ocean
and delivering it up to the upper regions of the atmosphere,
sixty or seventy miles above (see Fig. 8). The ordinary winds
then take hold of this fantastic machine and push it along
until either it strikes the shore (where it can cause great
devastation) or it encounters cooler waters, when it quickly
subsides.

3 Heat at work

Man first tamed fire about a quarter of a million years ago. Before that his entire life, when not actually hunting food, must have been taken up with eating it, so difficult must he have found it to masticate raw meat. Cooking not only develops the flavor of many foods, especially meat, it also renders them considerably easier to chew.

The cook is primarily concerned with applying heat to foodstuffs. She also applies many chemicals — salt (sodium chloride), acids such as vinegar and lemon juice, alkalis such as sodium bicarbonate — but her chief tool is a flame, and most of her "chemistry" is stimulated by heat.

Among the reactions that heat brings about in foodstuffs is the coagulating of protein in the white of an egg, the protein changing from a clear, almost colorless fluid to a white solid. Much more complex reactions occur when meat is cooked. First, there is the breakdown of protein molecules into smaller units; and, if water is used, there is reaction with the water (hydrolysis) that converts them into gelatin. Both processes can lead to a more tender meat. The heat also promotes reactions between chemicals in the meat; for example, one reaction responsible for much of the flavor of cooked meat takes place between a sugar called ribose and amino acids. Another source of flavor may be oxidation, a "rusting" of the meat that takes place during roasting, when the meat reacts with the hot air in the oven.

Likewise, foods of vegetable origin are made more palatable in the course of cooking. Such constituents as starch, in potatoes or rice, are made more soluble by boiling. The cell walls of many vegetables are ruptured in this process, and a hard brittle carrot is turned into a succulent vegetable. The same process applied to cabbage also liberates simple sulfur compounds, which provide the characteristic smell of cooking cabbage.

Most foods are rather sensitive to temperature, and those temperatures the cook employs are usually quite low on the scale we shall span in this section of the book (Fig. 9). Anyone who has burned a slice of toast or experienced the smell of burned fish in those countries which practice open-air charcoal cooking is well aware of the risks of overheating foodstuffs. Brandy poured over Christmas puddings or crêpes suzettes may yield spectacular flames but the temperatures generated are really quite low.

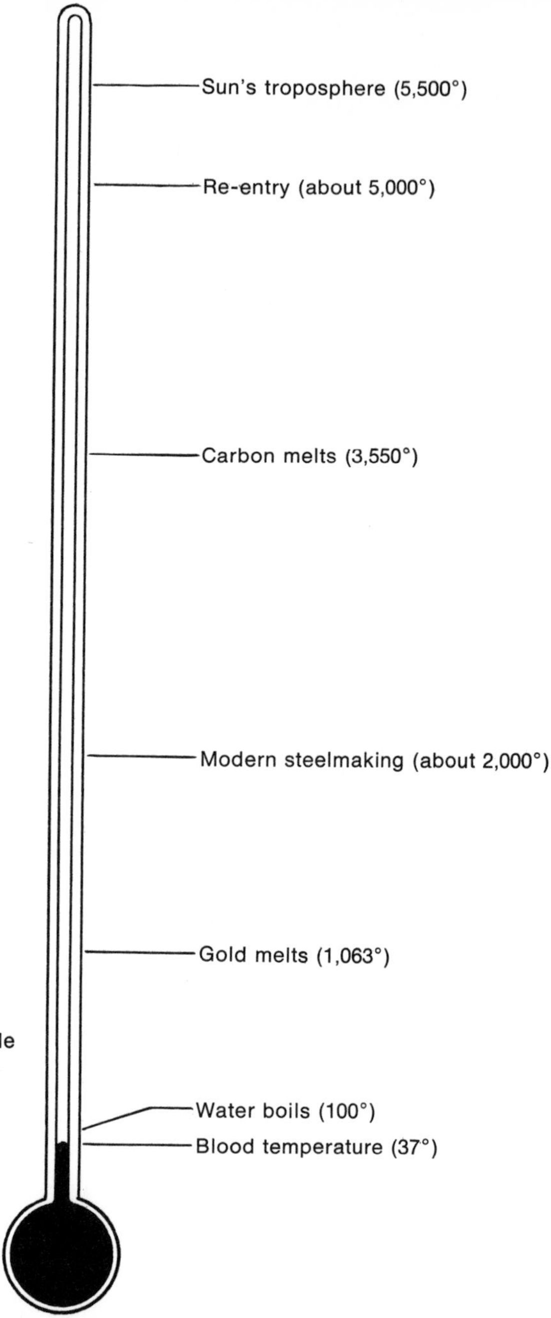

Sun's troposphere (5,500°)

Re-entry (about 5,000°)

Carbon melts (3,550°)

Modern steelmaking (about 2,000°)

Gold melts (1,063°)

Water boils (100°)

Blood temperature (37°)

FIG. 9. Centigrade (Celsius) Scale

Bubbling stills

One of the simplest and most widely used ways of separating two substances is to distill them; that is, to boil one off, as vapor, from the other. The idea was known to Alexandrian chemists nearly two thousand years ago, although another thousand years or more were to pass before the application arose for which it is best known today.

This application, of course, is the distillation of alcohol; a process so simple to perform that the Treasury Department must assign agents to check on the production of all stills. Spirits such as whisky and brandy, the basis of which is about 40 percent alcohol (ethyl alcohol, to use its chemical name), carry a high tax, and their distillation on any but authorized premises is highly illegal.

Distillation relies quite simply on a difference in boiling point between the substances to be separated. Water boils at 100°C., ethyl alcohol at 79°C.; and although the two clear, colorless liquids mix completely, they can be separated almost completely by carefully regulating the heat so that the mixture remains at between 80° and 90°C. Above the boiling mixture is arranged a condenser, whose temperature is held below the boiling point of water and above that of alcohol. Water, then, will condense on its surface and flow back into the boiling mixture, while alcohol vapor passes over to condense in another part of the apparatus and flow into a collecting vessel. The temperature of the mixture will rise steadily as more and more alcohol is distilled off until water alone remains.

This simple, elegant process is of immense industrial importance today. Thousands of gallons of whisky (and a small amount of moonshine, or illicit spirits) are distilled in this way, in stills of burnished copper. A vital part of the distiller's art lies in knowing how to permit just enough impurities to pass over with the alcohol to impart a distinctive flavor to the whisky or brandy.

For over a century now the oil industry has used this process to separate the various "fractions" or fluids of different density present in the sticky mixture known as crude oil. The lofty fractionating columns that grace a modern oil refinery are stills, so arranged that when the oil is boiled, a range of liquids are separated simultaneously, from the lightest (with the lowest boiling point) at the top to the heaviest (with the highest boiling point) at the bottom. Each fraction has its own application, from solvents to lubricants.

Materials of still higher boiling points, including such metals as mercury (which boils at $357°C.$) and zinc (which boils at $906°C.$) are separated industrially in this way by distilling them from their ores. Mercury, indeed, is often distilled in the laboratory in glass apparatus, for the method provides a ready way of purifying the liquid metal for its innumerable laboratory chores.

But the application which today excites greatest interest is the distillation of sea water to remove the 3.5 percent of salts that make it undrinkable. On a small scale this is done in many ways, some of which use the sun's heat. But a large plant for purifying sea water, yielding millions or even hundreds of millions of gallons of fresh water daily, such as parts of the Middle East, California, Peru and many other places would like to possess, raises formidable chemical engineering problems.

The most successful and economic solution yet in sight is an ingenious variation on the theme of distillation, a British invention called *multistage flash distillation,* in which a small amount of hot brine is "flashed" almost instantaneously into steam at each of many stages of distillation.

Atoms that strike sparks

Chemistry teaches us that there are 92 different kinds of atom to be found in nature (and a few more have been made artificially). But an enormous number of unstable varieties of these elements have also been made artificially in the last twenty-five years. These unstable species are called *radioisotopes;* they have the same chemical properties as the stable element but, because the nuclei of their atoms are overcrowded — they contain one or more extra neutrons — these atoms are unstable. As a result, they tend to break down, emitting radiation, rather like an atomic radio transmitter.

Radioisotopes can also be used to help the scientist measure intervals of time very accurately. There are many uses for the 1,300-odd radioisotopes that are known today, but here we shall consider just one: as sources of heat.

The radiations emitted by these unstable atoms are absorbed by other materials and changed into heat. Different radioisotopes give off different amounts of heat (see Photo 4). One radioisotope of the element curium, curium-242, is so unstable that a pellet weighing only one-third of an ounce glows white-hot.

One important thing about these radioisotopes is that many of them continue to emit heat for long periods — years, even

PHOTO 4. World's "hottest" piece of radioactive cobalt-60 boils the water in this beaker.

— with little change in output and none whatsoever in their volume. The earth itself, in fact, derives its own heat from a process of radioactive decay far beneath the earth's crust. By choosing a radioisotope with an output and a lifetime appropriate to the task, we have a most convenient source of heat for very many situations.

Some of the more important uses are in situations where it might be difficult if not impossible to supply ordinary fuels for long periods to generate the heat required. In space, for example, radioisotopes can be used to generate electricity if their heat is absorbed by materials that convert heat directly into electricity. One of the most successful systems is to employ a *thermoelectric* material. When very hot, such an arrangement can generate enough current to power a small radio transmitter.

Pocket-sized powerpacks of this kind may come to be as useful on the ground as in space, however. Already they are being installed in remote locations, often replacing cumbersome diesel generators, to provide light or a "bleep" from a buoy, power for automatic weather stations or radio stations in far-away places, or power for telephone repeaters and navigation aids on the ocean bed. Designs have been made which are expected to provide their power undiminished for ten years or more (see Photo 5).

There are even ideas for radioisotope generators that people might carry themselves. One is for a small heating system for skin divers that allows the diver to work under water for several hours. About 300 watts of heat from a backpack fueled with plutonium-238 is fed through fine tubes sewn into his diving suit.

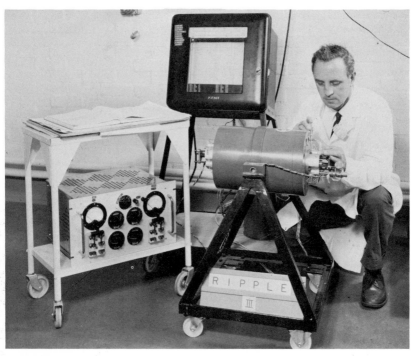

PHOTO 5. Isotopic powerpack undergoing final checks. A chart recorder for temperature can be seen behind the device.

Still more ambitious is a project to develop an istotopic source of power for the human body, to supply, say, an artificial heart. The idea here is actually to implant the radioisotope and the electricity generator inside the body along with the "spare part" it supplies. A heart pacemaker that draws power from this source has already been developed in the United States.

Chemistry of steelmaking .
Steel is far and away the most important engineering material and will remain so for a long time to come.

Steel is an alloy of carbon and iron, and was first made in Asia Minor about 1400 B.C. by heating wrought iron (a reasonably pure form of the element iron) with charcoal, a form of carbon obtained by burning wood. The amount and distribution of carbon in the iron are critically important to the steel's properties, and quite small differences will make the difference between the hard, brittle steel from which a sword or a razor is made, and the much softer steel used to make cars and tin cans.

The modern steelmaker first smelts iron from an iron-bearing rock or ore. This he does in the blast furnace, a tall tower which is filled with ore, coke and other materials. This mixture is heated at first with a flame, and air is blown in until the constituents are reacting together merrily, converting iron ore into molten iron. Once the mixture has been set alight, the chemical reactions give out enough heat to keep the whole furnace simmering at a temperature which ranges from about 250°C. at the top, where fresh material is being fed in, to 1,900°C. near the bottom, where the air is being blown in.

From such a furnace issues, every few hours, a stream of molten iron containing a variety of impurities, including too much carbon and silicon, sulphur and phosphorus. The next step in the steelmaking cycle is to purify this iron to leave precisely the kind of steel required.

Most of the world's steel is made by one of three processes:

1. The open hearth, in which the iron from the blast furnace is remelted in a large shallow pool, using ordinary natural gas to burn the impurities away.

2. The Bessemer process, in which compressed air is bubbled through a cauldron of molten steel.

49

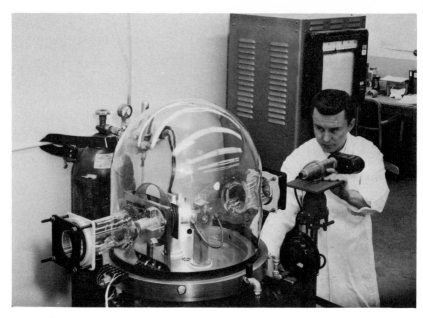

PHOTO 6. Optical pyrometer (*above right*) is used to measure the temperature of a molybdenum heater within the bell jar in this vacuum chamber apparatus.

3. The new electrical processes, such as one which uses a very powerful electric arc to melt and purify the metal.

Today, most steel is still made by the open-hearth process, but the importance of the other two methods is growing rapidly.

One of the most important advances in steelmaking was made in Austria little more than a decade ago, when steelmakers worked out a way of injecting oxygen instead of air into molten iron to purify it. Air, of course, is oxygen well diluted with nitrogen, so a much more energetic reaction might be expected if pure oxygen were used. In fact, with oxygen, steelmaking temperatures now reach 2,200°C., when iron can be purified in a fraction of the time previously needed

— fifteen minutes instead of an hour or more. The economic consequences of an increase of a few hundred degrees are immense.

So to some extent are the social consequences, for the new steelmaking methods using oxygen are far more scientifically based than the traditional process and cannot rely solely on the skills of the steelmaker. Very accurate control of temperature is needed if the ferocious reactions are not to get out of hand and eat up the melting pot.

Temperatures of this order are usually measured by an instrument called the *optical pyrometer,* which amplifies the eye's capacity to judge temperature at a distance by the color of the very hot metal. The optical pyrometer is illustrated in Photo 6 and sketched in Fig. 10. The brightness of a bulb,

FIG. 10. An optical pyrometer

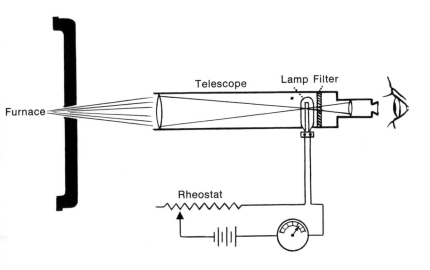

mounted in the telescope, is adjusted by means of the rheostat until it just blends with the background of molten metal.

Wholly satisfactory methods are still sought for measuring the temperature of the reacting metal and judging the exact point at which the steel is ready to be poured. One method that is being explored follows the sounds emitted by the bubbling steel and relates these to the temperature and the progress of the refining operation.

Treating with heat

But steel's association with heat does not end when the metal is poured into a mold. The likelihood is that the metal will be reheated to bright red heat, approaching 1,000 °C., to soften it for the next stage of working. In this condition it can be forged to the shape of a crankshaft or rolled out flat to a thin sheet of steel for a car body, drawn into wire or fashioned into a tube. Beyond this stage, when the steel has been forged or machined into the desired shape, heat plays a crucial role in developing precisely the properties the designer desires (Photo 7).

Heat treatment is the clue to the successful use of almost any metal in engineering, but none more so than steel. The relationship between iron and its other constituents, especially carbon, can be rearranged in innumerable ways to obtain the required blend of hardness, ductility and strength.

The simplest way of demonstrating the influence that heat treatment can exert on steel is to take a large nail, and heat it in a gas flame until it glows bright red, then plunge it into

PHOTO 7. White-hot metal specimen under examination for strength.

cold water. The nail, ordinarily ductile, becomes very hard. At the same time it becomes very brittle and if hammered into a piece of wood will probably snap off.

This simple process of hardening is widely employed in industry, usually to obtain a hard "skin" on a surface that is exposed to wear or abrasion. The teeth of hard-worked gear wheels provide a good example. They can be treated by exposing the contacting faces of each tooth briefly to a flame or some other carefully regulated source of heat, then quenching the hot tooth in water or oil (oil cools metal much more slowly, and the metal, although less hard, suffers less from shock). A hard "skin" forms on the flame-heated surfaces of each tooth.

But a piece of steel that has been hardened right through in this way is usually far too hard to be useful. It then has to be *annealed.* Annealing is a process which softens the metals and relieves the stresses that have built up in its structure. It calls for heating to a carefully chosen temperature, normally of a few hundred degrees, followed by leisurely cooling.

Annealing and nearly all other heat-treatment processes require very accurate knowledge of the metal's temperature. Once this used to be estimated by a skilled craftsman. He estimated high temperatures, for example, by judging the whiteness of the glow, and lower ones by watching the colors that run across the surface of a bright bit of metal as it gets hotter and hotter.

These *temper colors* range from pale straw at about 220°C. through purple at about 280°C. to a green-blue color at 320°C.

Rather more precise means include the use of temperature crayons, the marks from which melt at a known temperature.

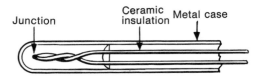

FIG. 11. Thermoelectric pyrometer or thermocouple

Another visual aid is little pyramids or cones composed of mixtures that begin to soften at a certain temperature; these are watched until the peaks keel over and collapse.

More accurate still, however, are the electrical methods of measurement, where heat is converted into an electrical signal, the strength of which is related to the temperature. The thermoelectric pyrometer, for example, is probably one of the most widely used methods of measuring furnace temperatures in industry or in the laboratory. This instrument employs the fact that when wires of two different metals are joined together and the joint is heated while the free ends are kept cool, a voltage is set up (Fig. 11). The strength of this voltage is related to the difference in temperature between the joint and the ends of the wires.

The beauty of the *thermocouple,* as the two-metal structure is called, is its versatility. By selecting suitable pairs of metals it can be adapted to a very wide range of temperatures and can also be made resistant to some extremely corrosive conditions. For the high temperatures and some most unpleasant conditions, precious metals such as platinum, iridium and rhodium are commonly used today, usually protected from direct contact with a molten metal or corrosive gas by a ceramic sheath. But a faster response to temperature changes is

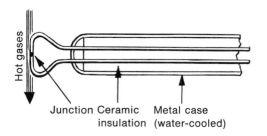

Junction Ceramic   Metal case
         insulation (water-cooled)

FIG. 12. Thermocouple with junction of wires exposed directly to heat

obtained, as you might expect, if the junction is exposed directly to the heat (Fig. 12).

But even metals as "noble" as these cannot withstand the temperatures encountered in the exhaust of a rocket engine, which may be 3,000°C. or more. Ingenious kinds of thermocouple instruments have been devised for this purpose, where a very carefully regulated flow of liquid whisks away the heat from the thermocouple junction before it can melt.

In the *cooled-tube thermometer* (Fig. 13), for example, the actual increase in temperature of the thermocouple junctions, which are kept immersed in water, may be only 100°C. Provided the speed of the exhaust gas can be measured, its temperature can be calculated accurately.

Very hot chemistry

Few steelmakers would regard themselves as chemists, but the steelmaking process is in a sense a chemical process carried out at very high temperature. Every modern steelmill uses the services of chemists, usually assisted by an instrument called the spectrophotometer, which is capable of analyzing

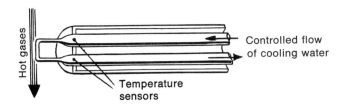

Controlled flow
of cooling water

Temperature
sensors

Hot gases

FIG. 13. Cooled-tube thermocouple thermometer

a small specimen of steel and telling the steelmaker, within about five minutes, exactly how much is present of a dozen or more elements. With this help the steelmaker can adjust the composition of his steel very precisely, and with a minimum of delay, before he pours.

The Swedish chemist Svante Arrhenius, who died in 1927, told us that the rate of speed of a chemical reaction will be in proportion to the number of collisions between reacting molecules. We have already seen in Chapter 2 that the hotter a substance, the more agitated its molecules become; hence the number of collisions increases. In fact, we find that the rate at which a chemical reaction proceeds roughly doubles for each ten-degree increase in temperature.

Professor Michael Dewar of the University of Texas has an unusual way of illustrating this fact. The life processes of the ant are chemical reactions and conform to the same laws as all chemistry. If you watch ants scurrying about their business, you find they run fast in sunshine, and slow down when they enter a patch of shade (see Fig. 14). And between 20°C. and 30°C., the speed of the ant roughly doubles. The ant can even serve as a thermometer, for by measuring the

FIG. 14. Movements of ants vary according to temperature

speed at which it moves it is possible to arrive at the temperature quite accurately.

The conclusion one might draw, of course, is that the faster the chemist (or rather, his industrial colleague, the chemical engineer) can arrange for his reaction to proceed, the quicker it will be completed and the more productive the process will be. This is precisely what happens when oxygen is used instead of air in steelmaking. In practice, very few chemical manufacturing processes exceed $500\,^{\circ}$C. Why, then, are not more processes operated at very high temperatures, taking minutes or even seconds to complete instead of hours or days?

The most obvious reason is the difficulty of containing a very hot chemical reaction — the difficulty of making a "test tube" that will stand up to the fierce heat and corrosion. Even in steelmaking the problems are by no means solved yet. But there are enterprising chemists who want to harness new sources of intense heat to chemical engineering.

Several sources are beginning to show high promise. One is the plasma torch, a product of the space-rocket laboratories, which we shall discuss a little later. Another is the electrically stimulated flame, which is a flame obtained from an ordinary fuel such as gas or oil and augmented with energy from an electrical source to temperatures reaching several thousand degrees Centigrade.

Another kind of very high-temperature "oven" is the *fluidized bed.* Imagine a column of sand, through which air is being blown. The column bubbles and seethes just as if it were boiling. If, instead of sand, grains of carbon are used, which are electrically conductive, the bubbling bed can be heated by passing a powerful electric current through it. Carbon will not melt, and temperatures beyond 3,000°C. can easily be attained. The gases that are to react together are simply blown through the glowing granules.

Higher still are the temperatures associated with a curious phenomenon known as the exploding wire. When a fuse wire is heavily overloaded by a bad short circuit, it may rupture with a bang, spattering molten metal around its protective casing. By abruptly discharging a very heavy current through a fine wire or foil, the metal can be exploded with great violence, generating a brilliant flash of light and setting up a powerful shock wave.

For a few millionths of a second the temperature of an exploding wire may reach a million degrees Centigrade. Chemists believe that reactions at such colossal temperatures will yield chemicals unobtainable in any other way.

Fourth state

After soaring briefly to a temperature of a million degrees Centigrade, we will slide back down to low thousands to discuss the origins and uses of one particular kind of high-temperature flame, the one that issues from a plasma torch. This will lead us into a discussion of the nature of plasma itself, and thence to nature's own plasma furnaces, the sun and the stars, and to man's efforts to emulate nature with thermonuclear reactions.

Plasma is a word more commonly associated with blood, and indeed it was coined over a century ago by the Czech biologist, Purkynic, to describe the jelly that makes up the bulk of the living cell. Irving Langmuir, a famous American physicist, adopted the term to describe something he regarded as "solid jelly": hot electrified gas, wherein atoms, molecules, electrons, ions and other molecular fragments jostle in frantic confusion.

There is terrific activity within a plasma, for the atomic species and subspecies are constantly splitting apart and recombining differently, with enormous exchanges of energy. The result is a searingly hot cloud. Plasma is sometimes called the fourth state of matter, the other three being solid, liquid and gas.

Such a cloud envelopes a spacecraft when it reenters the earth's atmosphere, owing to an intense friction with air molecules — the *Apollo* mooncraft will reenter the atmosphere at a speed of nearly seven miles a *second*. The cloud scrambles radio waves and so prevents contact between the spacecraft and the tracking stations on the ground for a few crucial moments.

It was the need to investigate this process — which entails great risks for the contents of a spacecraft or a missile — on a laboratory scale that led American space engineers to develop the plasma generator, that is, a controllable source of very intense heat. The plasma "flame" takes over roughly at the top limit of chemical flames.

Essentially a plasma generator, although there are many kinds, is an electric arc device, that is to say, a device that makes use of a sustained flow of electricity across a small gap. Whereas the upper limit of temperature for an electric arc is usually put around 5,000°C., plasma can be squirted from a suitably arranged arc at anything from 1,500°C. to 50,000°C. The knack, in part, is to design a generator that does not just eat itself up.

The most powerful plasma generators in existence today are those used in rocket test laboratories. The largest of these *hyperthermal* tunnels, used to test the effects of reentry on missile nose cones and spacecraft heat shields (see Photo 8), consume the output of a substantial power station. One industrial application for these very powerful plasma generators promises to be big plasma furnaces that will melt and refine metals, especially hard-to-melt metals such as tungsten (melting point 3,400°C.) and molybdenum (melting point 2,600°C.), much more rapidly than an ordinary high-temperature furnace.

But space technology also promises to find a direct application of a jet of plasma: to drive a spacecraft. The technology of electric rockets, which produce a small but continuous thrust, probably with electricity that comes from solar cells, is the most likely solution to the powering of a spacecraft once it has left the earth's environs. It may also be the most efficient way of maneuvering a satellite into the most satisfactory orbit.

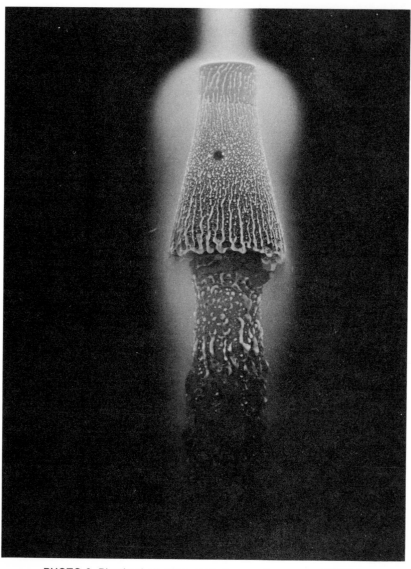

PHOTO 8. Plastic shell exposed to temperatures near 5,000°C.

One electric rocket system is, in effect, a plasma torch which converts electric power into a steady stream of atomic fragments that are ejected from a nozzle like the exhaust from a chemical rocket.

The chemist has other ideas for the highly excited conditions within a cloud of plasma, for it offers him a "reaction vessel" that he cannot create in any other way. Plasma chemistry, at temperatures which no solid substances can ever exist, may set off reactions that are difficult, even impossible, at lower temperatures. Valuable industrial chemicals such as acetylene, cyanogen and hydrogen cyanide can be synthesized in the plasma. Someday it may be possible to spray powdered metal ores straight into a jet of plasma and collect the molten metal in a highly purified state.

At its most practical level, perhaps, the plasma torch has already found extensive use as a hand tool for welding and cutting metals and for spraying materials with coatings of ceramic. But an application that demonstrates rather neatly just how much control can now be exercised over this ferocious source of heat is provided by an American surgeon. Dr. Charles Sheer of Columbia University is developing a plasma scalpel that will simultaneously cut and cauterize living tissues.

Sun in harness

From a distance of 93 million miles shines a vast globe of plasma, nearly a million miles in diameter, the furnace that heats and lights the earth itself, and indeed from which the earth originally came. But so vast is the mass of the sun, about one-third of a million times the mass of our own planet, that its plasma is compressed to a density greater than that of water. The outermost temperature of the sun is around 5,500 °C. and even those cool dark patches we know as sun spots are about 4,000 °C., while temperatures deep within this plasma furnace approach 15 million °C.

No ordinary process of combustion could sustain this temperature. The processes within are known as *thermonuclear* reactions and involve the transmutation of hydrogen into helium, a most unreactive substance that remains unaffected even at such colossal temperatures. The same kind of reactions that take place inside the sun, and inside every other star (for the sun is a fairly typical star), man now achieves in the detonations of a hydrogen bomb. The H-bomb employs an atomic bomb of uranium or plutonium to generate a temperature high enough to set the thermonuclear reactions going.

But a thermonuclear reaction triggered in this way is far too boisterous for engineers to hope to harness the heat. Far more sophisticated methods are needed to heat a plasma up to the millions of degrees necessary to set off such a reaction. The plasma must simultaneously be heated and squeezed to increase its density, in which condition it becomes a remarkably unstable substance. One, moreover, that will instantly vaporize any substance with which it makes contact, at the same time losing its own colossal temperature.

The only known way to contain a wildly threshing plasma of this kind, however fleetingly, is within a "bottle" formed by powerful magnetic fields.

It may be another thirty years or more before electric power is generated from a thermonuclear reaction. All the signs are that the technology will be immensely difficult. But the incentive to battle with those difficulties becomes plain once you appreciate how cheap electric power could become as a result. Hydrogen, the thermonuclear fuel, is one of the most commonplace elements on earth, indeed, in the universe. The sea alone contains five percent hydrogen by weight.

Someday a tiny synthetic "sun," safely bottled at the heart of a gigantic power station, will bring energy abundantly and cheaply to our planet.

4 Frost at work

If your body gets cold it is normally the extremities — toes and fingers, ears and nose — that suffer first. These are the parts farthest from the heart, where the blood's circulation has become rather sluggish. These, then, are the parts most likely to suffer frostbite should the body become so cold that crystals of ice start to form between the living cells. Frostbite is a constant hazard to soldiers serving in rigorous climates and to mountaineers.

But the injury is usually a much less serious matter today than it was in the nineteenth century. For one thing, the infection that caused so much suffering then is now fairly easily controlled, while injured tissue can often be completely restored by drugs that stimulate the blood circulation and by such treatment as exposing the frostbitten areas to oxygen under pressure.

More common than frostbite, however, is another consequence of the body's growing very cold. Doctors call this condition *hypothermia,* which simply means *below temperature.*

"Freezing to death," an expression we often use loosely, can be a very serious matter for elderly people and even, it has recently been found, for young healthy people under certain circumstances. Dr. Lewis Pugh, a physiologist who works for the Medical Research Council in London, recently analyzed twenty-three cases of overexposure, some of them fatal ones, and found that a particular condition, called accidental hypothermia, can arise when the body loses heat at a quite alarming rate.

Usually the victim is walking or climbing in cold, rainy weather and has become soaked to the skin. If a cold wind is blowing, heat can drain from the body very quickly — so fast, in fact, that the walker may collapse and die within an hour or two. The same thing may happen if a person, however hardy, pushes himself to the point of physical collapse while wet and cold.

Soldiers and mountaineers have been among the victims. As you might expect, thin people are more vulnerable than plump ones, and men are more vulnerable than women, who are protected by having more fatty tissues. Cases have been recorded of victims, deeply unconscious, whose body temperatures were too low to register on a clinical thermometer.

Dr. Pugh, an authority on physical exhaustion, advises certain elementary precautions for anyone who may become exposed. For prevention, he recommends that walkers, climbers, yachtsmen, and so on, carry light waterproof outer garments of plasticized nylon, preferably in bright colors to help would-be rescuers. And suppose hypothermia has actually begun? He says that "when a person shows early symptoms of exposure, the surest way of preventing disaster is to camp. . . ." And the cure for accidental hypothermia is to warm the victim up again with hot water or hot baths as soon as possible.

Plants, too, suffer from the cold, as any gardener knows only too well; but there is already some promise that "frosticides" may be developed to give the plant extra resistance. These are chemicals which help to reduce the risk of ice crystals forming between and within the cell walls of the plant. Such chemicals, if they prove both successful and cheap, may become very important to farmers and indeed to whole nations whose prosperity may depend upon the success or failure of a single crop.

Cold surgery

There are occasions when the surgeon finds it valuable to cool the body a few degrees below the normal temperature of $37°C$. (see Photo 9). For instance, the brain will normally suffer damage if deprived of its blood supply for more than three to five minutes, but if the body is cooled to $29°C$. the circulation can be interrupted for as much as ten minutes. This much "refrigeration" can easily be induced by a special kind of drug that anesthetizes the patient. But it is done much

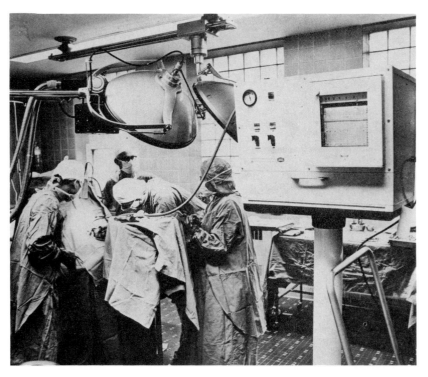

PHOTO 9. Cryosurgical apparatus in use in an operating room.

more slowly and carefully than happens in accidental hypo-thermia.

Even lower temperatures can be reached safely by cooling the patient's blood. The widely publicized "heart-lung" machine, with the help of which some remarkable heart surgery has been achieved in recent years, permits a machine to take over the task of pumping the blood and renewing its oxygen supply, removing the risk the heart itself runs of stopping if it gets too cold. But by passing the blood through a cooling apparatus as well, the body temperature can safely be reduced to about 15 °C.

The frozen limit

We have already seen, by various examples, that the temperature range that human beings can tolerate is very narrow; and indeed this applies to most forms of life. But one of the lowest kinds of living organism, bacteria (or microbes), can survive a much wider range (although as we shall see they may be active only when warm). Bacteria are responsible for many diseases — tuberculosis and whooping cough, for example; they are also responsible for the deterioration of food and hence for the food poisoning that may follow the eating of bad foods.

There is a very simple way of holding bacteria in check, however: cooling the food sufficiently to inactivate them. Bacterial breeding falls off dramatically as the temperature is lowered below room temperature, and food that normally will go bad in a few hours on a hot summer's day will keep for days at 0° to 10°C. (that is, 273 to 283°K: to avoid negative temperatures we will stick to the Kelvin scale throughout this part of the book — see Fig. 5), because the number of bacteria multiplies so rapidly.

Ice-making machines were patented in America in the 1830's. In 1877 frozen mutton was brought by sea from the Argentine to France in a journey which, because of a collision, took six months. The meat kept in excellent condition, nonetheless. By the turn of the century special freighters with refrigerated holds were shipping not only meat but dairy produce, fruit and vegetables around the world.

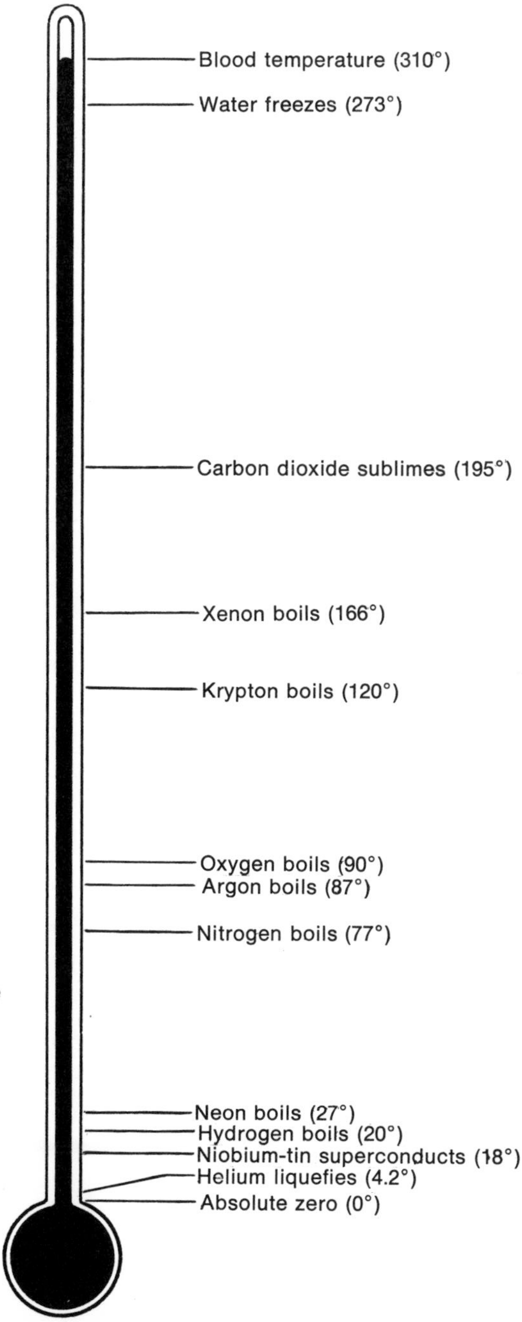

FIG. 15. Kelvin Scale

Blood temperature (310°)
Water freezes (273°)
Carbon dioxide sublimes (195°)
Xenon boils (166°)
Krypton boils (120°)
Oxygen boils (90°)
Argon boils (87°)
Nitrogen boils (77°)
Neon boils (27°)
Hydrogen boils (20°)
Niobium-tin superconducts (18°)
Helium liquefies (4.2°)
Absolute zero (0°)

Any well-equipped kitchen today will contain a refrigerator capable of cooling food down to about the freezing point of water. Some possess a deep freeze, the temperature of which may reach $195\,°K.$, the temperature at which the gas carbon dioxide freezes. Carbon dioxide is an oddity in that it cannot normally be liquefied, but changes straight from gas to solid and vice versa. This is why frozen carbon dioxide is popularly known as dry ice.

Cold engines

Let us see how we might make a machine that produces cold.

The simplest kind of refrigerator consists of nothing more than a piston and cylinder. When the piston rises in the cylinder, the air trapped within is compressed and becomes very hot. This is because the movement of the piston is adding energy to the gas molecules. In a diesel engine the very hot air is used to ignite a squirt of fuel. Instead, let us cool the cylinder with water and take away the extra heat the piston has added. If, now, we withdraw the piston so that the air can expand once more to its original volume, we find the air molecules are left in a far more sluggish condition. In other words, they have lost energy and grown colder.

This is a process which can easily be made continuous, although in this fairly crude form it is not very convenient to reach temperatures much below the freezing point of water. But we can make a big refinement by allowing our compressed but cooled gas to escape continuously through a fine nozzle. Nearly every home refrigerator, electric or gas, works in this way. The process is sketched in Fig. 16.

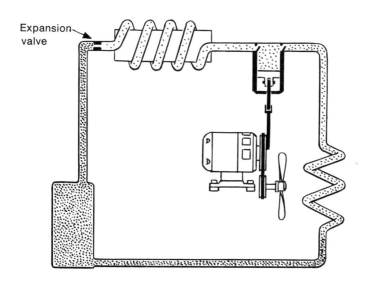

FIG. 16. How a refrigerator works

To plunge more deeply into the so-called *cryogenic* regions (*cryo* comes from a Greek word meaning frost) we can adapt the same process. For gases that liquefy at the temperature of liquid nitrogen (77.3 °K.) or above, cold water is all that is necessary as the coolant for the compressed gas. But if we want to liquefy hydrogen (20.5 °K.), we must cool the compressed gas with liquid nitrogen. And to reach the point of liquefaction for helium, 4.2°K., we use liquid hydrogen as the coolant.

More efficient, however, than a piston-and-cylinder type of compressor at very low temperatures and very high pressures is the turbine. To work efficiently, the turbine has to be extremely small and extremely fast, but some marvelous examples of precision engineering have emerged in recent years, only an inch or so in diameter and spinning at several thousand revolutions a *second.*

Usually we think of a refrigerator, for whatever purpose, as a large bulky affair, so the actual size of the cold engine would not seem to matter greatly. But there is a growing demand for very small sources of extreme cold where, for one reason or another, it is inconvenient simply to surround things with, say, liquid nitrogen or liquid helium. Examples can be found in electronic equipment, in the cooling of specimens for examination under the electron microscope, and in computers that work at very low temperatures.

Microminiature refrigerators are being developed for many of these applications which squeeze the machinery into an incredibly small volume (Photo 10). But there is an electronic process for generating cold that may prove more compact, efficient and convenient in many instances. It was a French watchmaker named Jean Peltier who first observed the process.

In Chapter 3 we noted the thermocouple as a means of measuring temperature: two different metals, when joined, produced a voltage that grew stronger and stronger as the temperature increased. But Peltier found that if instead a current is passed through two such wires, the joint grows either hotter or colder, depending on which way the current is flowing.

Unfortunately, the differences in temperature that we can obtain in this way are quite small, a few degrees only, partly because metals are too similar electronically, and partly because they are excellent conductors of heat, and any temperature difference between the ends of the wires is soon balanced out.

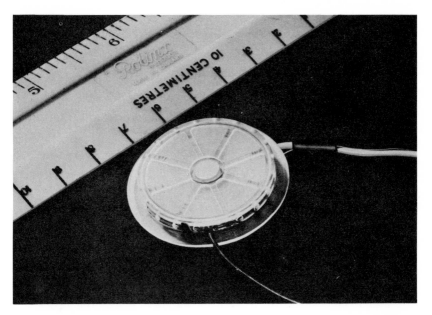

PHOTO 10. This little refrigerator can cool a piece of equipment — an electronic component, for example — from room temperature to −186°C. within two seconds.

But far greater cooling effects have been discovered in a kind of material called a *semiconductor,* a substance whose electrical properties lie midway between those of metals and those of nonmetals such as glass and china. Two examples are silicon and germanium, the materials from which transistors are made. Very large cooling effects can be obtained from certain semiconductors, when fashioned into special shapes.

Keeping things cold

To anything that is very cold, down around the temperature of liquid hydrogen or liquid helium, ordinary temperatures as we know them seem just like a very hot furnace. A drop of liquid air or oxygen poured from its flask onto the floor vaporizes in a puff of white "steam," much as a drop of cold water behaves when spilled on a hot stove. If we want our cryogenic liquids to survive until we are ready to use them, we must find some very efficient way of insulating them from the "furnace" outside that surrounds them.

Sir James Dewar, a professor of chemistry in London and the man who first liquefied hydrogen in 1898, also invented one of the most efficient kinds of low-temperature insulation. The Dewar flask, as it is known, is familiar to all of us as the thermos bottle, in which we can keep beverages such as hot coffee or cold milk at the same temperature for hours at a stretch.

Dewar flasks and thermos bottles — they are really the same thing — consist of two vessels, one inside the other, with the air pumped out from the space between them. A vacuum is a remarkably efficient insulator, for few air molecules are available to transfer heat by conduction or convection (see Chapter 2). The third method of heat transfer, radiation, can be suppressed by providing the glass of the inner bottle with a bright mirror-like surface that simply bounces the radiating heat back again.

Difficulties intrude, however, if we want to make a large Dewar flask to store hundreds or even thousands of gallons of liquefied gas. Nowadays this situation is quite common in rocket technology, for example, and in steelmaking. The problem is how to sustain a very good vacuum around a very large "flask." But we can actually make do with much less of a vacuum if we pack the insulating space with certain powdered minerals.

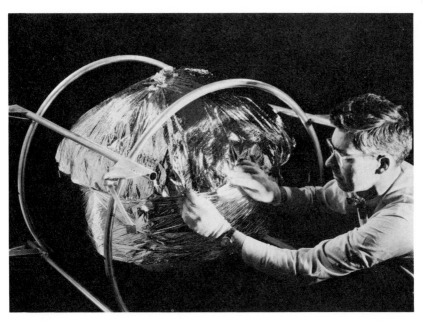

PHOTO 11. Superinsulation for a spacecraft, composed of a plastic film coated with an extremely thin layer of aluminum.

But even this measure is inadequate for the two coldest liquids, hydrogen and helium. One answer, the expensive one, is to surround them with a third vessel that contains liquid nitrogen. Cheaper and more efficient is the use of a *super-insulant,* a thin crumpled foil, usually of aluminum or a plastic with a shiny metallic surface, packed into the insulating space (Photo 11).

A Swedish invention, superinsulation can provide us with large containers in which liquid helium can be shipped thousands of miles with evaporation losses no greater than 1 or 2 percent a day. This is remarkable progress compared with the transportation of compressed helium gas in heavy steel "bottles."

Kept "on ice"

An enterprising company has recently offered to sell people space for their bodies after death in a morgue they plan to construct in Antarctica, the idea being that the very low temperature would preserve the bodies until such time as science produces a method of bringing a corpse back to life!

However this may be, *living* cells can certainly be preserved almost indefinitely if cooled to very low temperatures. Nitrogen liquefies at $77\,^{\circ}$K. (Fig. 15), and as it is chemically a very inactive substance it provides a very useful way of cold-storing biological materials. One very important material now stored at such temperatures is blood.

Blood is a most complicated fluid, really a living organ of the body. It can be astonishingly sensitive to many kinds of contamination. Normally in a blood transfusion the patient is given fresh blood plasma (a concentrated version of fresh blood) that has been stored in a refrigerator. But fresh blood will not keep for more than about three weeks.

A new technique has recently been invented in the United States and Britain, in which the principal ingredients of fresh blood are separated and frozen by a technique that prevents ice crystals from forming in the cells and rupturing them. The blood is frozen in liquid nitrogen at $77\,^{\circ}$K. Blood frozen in this way can be kept for two years or more, an enormous advantage to hospitals which otherwise must continually discard their unused blood supplies.

Living tissues of many kinds can be preserved in this way, by a process known as *freeze drying,* the essence of which is to cool the tissue quickly enough to prevent the growth of ice crystals in the cells, for it is their growth that ruptures the cell walls and kills the tissue. The tissue is then kept at a higher temperature, under vacuum, while the still microscopic crystals of ice "sublime," or turn straight into vapor without first melting. You can observe this process on a frosty day, when wet laundry will freeze stiff then gradually thaw out and become limp without ever becoming damp again.

Freeze drying promises to develop into an important process for two entirely different purposes. One is the preservation of living tissues and, someday, living organs for transplantation by surgeons into other people's bodies. Bone and blood vessels are already preserved in this way. The second process is the preservation of foods for very long periods with little or no loss of flavor, texture or "goodness."

Cold out here

One thing we know about space is how extremely cold it is. The moon, which lacks the remarkably effective insulation that our atmosphere provides for the earth, cycles between a surface temperature at noon that exceeds water's boiling point and a nighttime low of around $140\,^\circ$K. As we go farther from the sun, the planet's temperatures plunge still lower: Jupiter is believed to have a surface temperature of $135\,^\circ$K., Saturn a maximum of $120\,^\circ$K., and Pluto, at a distance of 3,666 million miles from the sun, an average temperature of only $63\,^\circ$K.

Craft that venture into space must be constructed to cope with very low temperatures, a situation that can raise problems totally unlike any encountered on earth. Metals such as steel can develop an alarmingly brittle condition; many plastics and rubber can also. Lubricants may freeze to glasslike solids, and coolants may no longer circulate.

In order to test space "hardware" under conditions as near as possible to those which obtain in space, the space engineers have set up great space simulators — chambers in which equipment from individual components to an entire spacecraft can be assembled and run under any condition they may expect to encounter. To simulate the coldness of "black space," for example, the apparatus under test will be surrounded with black surfaces, cooled by liquid nitrogen boiling away at the rate of hundreds of gallons an hour. The Dutch have built a big space chamber at the Space Center at Noordwijk in Holland, which will reproduce temperatures from $77°$ to $400°K$.

But rocket engineers have quite another interest in very low temperatures, for the liquefaction of gases such as oxygen and hydrogen provides a convenient way of compressing these powerful fuels into a small volume. Small relatively, that is, since the *Saturn V* rocket that will carry the *Apollo* spacecraft and its three astronauts to the moon will swallow ten tons of liquid oxygen every *second* for the first 150 seconds of its journey.

The need to store and to regulate the flow of these extremely cold liquids with utter reliability has invoked a whole new branch of engineering, cryoengineering. We have already noted one very important consequence of cryoengineering in Chapter 3, for liquid oxygen is now used in enormous quantities in almost every modern steelmill in the world.

Frozen chemistry

An increase of only ten degrees doubles the rate of chemical reaction, as is discussed in Chapter 3. It would be reasonable to expect, therefore, that at the temperature of liquid air, $78°$ K., chemical reactivity has been slowed down to a rate which is very slow indeed. Curiously enough, this is not so.

Chemistry is by no means as simple or tidy as the textbook formulas seem to make it. A seemingly straightforward reaction, in which two reagents combine to form two different substances, may in reality involve the formation of all sorts of in-between products. But when the dust settles, we are left only with the two products described by the chemical equation, which is often all we really need to know. When chemistry is carried out at very low temperatures, however, some of the very unstable "intermediates" are found to be much more stable. Their presence often becomes apparent as strange and wonderful colors, sometimes as powerful and unexpected explosions or flare-ups.

A few years ago rocket engineers became very interested in *cryochemistry,* or very low temperature chemistry, where highly unstable chemicals were frozen into a state of comparative stability. This was a field first explored in 1885 by Sir James Dewar, inventor of the Dewar flask, and later by the French scientist, Henri Moissan. One consequence of recent interest has been the discovery of a blood-red liquid called ozone difluoride, which exists only at temperatures below

90°K. One of the most powerful chemicals ever found, ozone difluoride ignites or explodes spontaneously when it comes into contact with many substances, even at very low temperatures. It is thus a potential rocket fuel.

From the viewpoint of the scientist, however, very low temperatures give an opportunity to study reactions such as combustions and explosions which normally take place too quickly for the chemistry of the process to be examined very carefully. Applied in another way, the techniques of low-temperature chemistry should help us to understand what goes on at the surface of very cold planets such as Jupiter and those beyond. Jupiter itself possesses richly colored bands that come and go, and also the once-Great Red Spot, now fading fast. Both phenomena may well be explained by atmospheric chemistry that could occur only in an extremely cold climate. Jupiter's surface temperature is believed to be about 135°K., and its atmosphere is rich in methane and ammonia.

Superconductors

Chapter 2 of this book discussed the resistance thermometer, which allows us to measure temperature extremely accurately, simply by measuring the resistance a piece of wire offers to an electric current at a given temperature. The electrical resistance of every metal increases as its temperature rises and, of course, falls as its temperature is lowered. This statement holds true down to extremely low temperatures. Then something truly astonishing may happen.

There comes a point with many metals and alloys where

every trace of electrical resistance abruptly vanishes. This point is not, as you might expect, absolute zero — which is unobtainable anyway, as we already know — but a few degrees above.

The practical consequences of this most curious event are tremendous, for it is the presence of resistance in a metal that means that we must constantly exert energy if we want to force an electric current through the metal. Take away this resistance, and the current will continue to flow with little or no further effort from without.

Let us take the example of mercury, for this was the metal in which an eminent Dutchman, Heike Kamerlingh Onnes, of the University of Leiden, in 1911 found that resistance could be made to disappear. First we make a ring of this silvery fluid and freeze it to the temperature of liquid helium. (Onnes, incidentally, was the man who first liquefied helium, last of the gases to succumb, in 1908.)

Now if we pass an electric current into the solid mercury and then disconnect the battery, the current continues to flow (we can easily detect its flowing without actually touching the mercury ring). Provided the mercury were never allowed to warm up, the current would still be flowing years later, undiminished in strength.

One possible use for this strange behavior, called *superconductivity,* was soon thought up by Kamerlingh Onnes. It was to make a really powerful electromagnet, or solenoid. Strong magnets were very valuable tools of scientists, but a really powerful one not only consumes enough electricity to supply a small town but it needs a river of water to keep it cool enough. A magnet coil in which an electric current circulated endlessly, wasting none of its strength in generating unwanted heat, was indeed a most tantalizing prospect.

Tantalizing it was to remain, too; for an enormous snag that no one could have foreseen now appeared. The very presence of a strong magnetic field caused the metal coils to revert to their normal stage of electrical resistance. They simply switched back again, as abruptly as they had switched to a superconducting state. Another half century was to pass before a substance was discovered that not only became a superconductor at a certain very low temperature but remained so despite the presence of a powerful magnetic field.

But in 1961, J. E. Kunzler, a scientist at the famous Bell Telephone Laboratories in New York, announced that he had found an alloy of the two metals niobium and tin which behaved as a so-called *high-field superconductor*. Others soon followed, and today engineers have a variety of these superconductors available for experiments in designing electrical machines of remarkable power and efficiency (Photo 12).

I say "experiments," for there is a long way to go before these superconducting machines become really practical. But small yet astonishingly powerful magnet coils have already been wound and are used in many scientific experiments. These magnets, the running costs of which are chiefly the cost of keeping them at liquid helium temperature, may soon find engineering uses in space, perhaps to keep lethal radiations at bay, and in machinery to provide frictionless bearings that "float" in a field of magnetism. More efficient ways of generating, transmitting and using electric current are among the many possibilities for the future.

PHOTO 12. Making tests on a specimen of superconducting material. The specimen is about to be lowered into a Dewar flask of liquid helium that will cool it close to absolute zero.

Near absolute zero

For all practical purposes the boiling point of liquid helium, 4.2 °K., represents about the lowest temperature we can hope to use industrially. In the last few years there has been a very rapid increase in the amount of liquid helium used — so much so that today scientists can have Dewars of helium delivered daily by a new kind of "milk round." Nowadays the curious behavior of liquid helium can easily be demonstrated by means of a demonstration kit specially made for schools.

But for more than half a century now there has been intense scientific interest in attaining temperatures far below this, simply because the less agitated a substance's atomic lattice becomes, the more information the scientist is likely to glean from it.

In fact, it is relatively easy to reduce the temperature to about 0.8 °K., if we use a sufficiently powerful pump to draw off the evaporating helium, just as we do with the vapor of other gases in the less cold refrigerators we discussed earlier.

To reach below 0.8 °K. scientists have discovered they can make use of a rare and costly kind of helium known as helium-3. Obtained from the radioactive decay of a radioisotope of lithium, this "light helium" costs about $150 a pound, compared with about 7 cents a pound for ordinary helium (helium-4). Light helium boils at 3 °K., and by pumping alone a temperature of 0.35 °K. can be reached. But by remarkably ingenious use of both forms of helium, far lower temperatures are now possible.

These temperatures, as low as 0.05 °K., are reached in what has been claimed as the first entirely new refrigeration cycle for many years. Invented by three British scientists led by Dr.

Heinz London of the Atomic Energy Research Establishment at Harwell, the new refrigerator employs the *superfluidity* of helium, probably the first application ever of this strange phenomenon.

Superfluidity is a condition achieved by one liquid only, helium-4, and then only when it is cooled below $2.2\,^\circ$K. When so cooled, however, helium becomes remarkably fluid, gushing through the finest crack or tiniest hole, and even emptying itself from a beaker by climbing the walls and running down the outside of the glass.

The idea behind the refrigerator is to use as the evaporating liquid a very cold mixture of the two kinds of helium, helium-3 and helium-4. When cooled below about $0.9\,^\circ$K., the mixture separates into two "liquids," one above the other. On the top is a liquid that is rich in helium-3, on the bottom one rich in helium-4. But the bottom phase becomes superfluid at this temperature, and the atoms of light helium "see" this phase not as a liquid but as a gas. If light helium can now be induced, by pumping, to pass continuously from the upper to the lower liquid, a situation analogous to evaporation is produced — except that the light helium "evaporates" *downward*. This is what the new refrigerator does, with the help of some very delicate plumbing.

So far as we know, there is no hope of reducing the temperature any further by evaporation. To reach nearer to absolute zero, scientists have to make use of quite different principles, such as the magnetic properties of materials.

Many chemical compounds behave as though they were composed of microscopic magnets, all pointing in different directions. If crystals of such a compound are cooled as far as possible by evaporation and then exposed to a very powerful magnetic field, all the microscopic magnets tend to line up. There is a sharp drop in the crystals' temperature as this happens.

What in fact has happened, of course, is that the atomic arrangement of the crystals has become more orderly and a little more heat has been squeezed out by the magnetic field.

The same approach applied not to metallic atoms (the microscopic magnets) but to the nuclei of the atoms, has plunged the temperature still nearer the unattainable. Dr. Nicholas Kurti in the Clarendon Laboratory at Oxford University, one of the world's most famous low-temperature laboratories, in 1963 managed to reach as low as one millionth of a degree in this way.

This may at last be the limit, unless scientists discover some other "subatomic" mechanism with which they can bring a little more order out of nature's chaos.

Index

Index

About the Author

DAVID FISHLOCK, the editor of the *Yardsticks of Science* Series, was graduated from the Bristol College of Technology in England. He began writing in 1954, when he started contributing articles to technical magazines. He then became a staff writer on the *New Scientist* and later the magazine's technology editor. He has also worked as an electrochemist for the Westinghouse Brake and Signal Company.

Mr. Fishlock has traveled widely through many countries in Europe, Africa, and the Far East. He belongs to the Association of British Science Writers and the Research and Development Society. In his spare time he enjoys listening to music.

DATE DUE

MY 18 '94			

DEMCO 38-297